Are You Mas[k]

Feelings about COVID-19

Story by: Robika Mylroie PhD • Rachael Whitaker PhD • Anna Selby PhD

This book is dedicated to the five
little humans in our lives with big emotions.
For all they've taught us and all they plan to teach us.

Special thanks to Felicia De Rosa with Codex Art &
Apparel for the beautiful illustrations and Evan
Unverdorben at Codex Art & Apparel for all that he and
his team did (his patience with us)!

This is a work of creative fiction though the feelings within this story are very real for many children, adolescents and even adults.

First Edition

Cover design and illustrations by Codex Art & Apparel

Please visit our Facebook page at
https://www.facebook.com/loveyoumorebooks

Lala was in 2nd grade;

she'd been having fun all year.

Then she heard a brand new word

that made all the fun seem to disappear.

Coronavirus, it was called;

it sounded mighty strange.

Then suddenly, to her surprise,

her world began to change!

She didn't get to say goodbye

to teachers or her friends.

Ballet, gymnastics and soccer -

it all came to an end!

Lala's parents watched the news,

and everything she'd see

was sadness, anger, loss, and pain.

She started fearing the tv!

But sometimes it was on all day.

Her parents did not observe

Lala started changing!

She began to lose her nerve.

In an attempt to reconnect,

Lala tried to virtually meet.

She could call her friends throughout the day.

It was a needed treat!

When Lala talked with friends

she found, to her surprise,

they all felt the same way.

COVID was scary in all their eyes!

Parents started to work from home,

it felt like a party everyday.

Unless they had a meeting,

which really got in the way!

Darby started noticing

she felt a bit askew.

Her moods were on a see-saw,

Up or down? She never knew.

Ava and Asher were a little older.

Siblings were these two.

When Corona hit their house

the place became a zoo!

Their parents would say, "Go outside!

But stay away from Mary.

Her mom could get really sick

If COVID you did carry."

Even though their feelings
were not all the same,
she knew it was important
that each feeling had a name.

Lala sat her parents down;

she expressed her fears.

Her parents then held her tight

and let her cry her tears.

Her parents hadn't realized

there was something wrong.

She'd kept her feelings inside -

they were there all along.

They did not try to talk her out

of the feelings that she had,

Instead they offered love to her.

She began to feel less sad.

Emotions can seem scary

if you hold them in.

When you unmask your feelings

the healing can begin!

Masks can come in different styles:

anger, fear or worry.

It's all about the reaching out

that gives your emotions a voice in a hurry.

Lala's nerve every now and then

sometimes wants to leave.

She talks it out with her parents now

and her nerve she can retrieve!

My advice is find a person

to whom you can talk.

A counselor, parent, teacher, or friend

to support your emotional walk.

What Does Your Child's Emotional Walk Look Like?

From the Parent side of our hearts: Our hope in writing this story is to bring a conversation to the table for you and your children; going on an "emotional walk" with them as they work through their feelings. As adults, we often forget that children hear and see things of which we are unaware. Especially during these times, children are feeling scared, angry, anxious, fearful, confused, excited, concerned, brave and vulnerable. These mixed feelings can become confusing, and sometimes hard to understand. Giving our children the power to process and name these feelings as well as learn to take control while understanding their emotions is the biggest gift we can give our children. These are moments our children can learn so many valuable, lifelong lessons. Even as adults, we sometimes forget to listen to our emotions. We hope this book can empower us all to practice conversations around our feelings. The most important thing we can do as adults is to listen to these little humans with big emotions and not try to solve their problems. We may not have all the answers; but being honest and transparent with our feelings is the path to connection. Who doesn't want to feel connected?

From the Counselor side of our hearts: This book is designed not just to support emotions around COVID-19, but to show how process and talking really works. Hopefully you can use this book and its illustrations to talk about bigger feelings, present or past. Consider allowing the child to become Lala in the story thinking through how they would process these big feelings. You can also use the other characters in the story to teach how to be a supportive friend/adult when you see others struggling with big emotions. After working through tough feelings consider what your child enjoys: art, reading, music, exercise to name a few. Allow them some time and space to do something positive. Talk about what they did and how they felt before and after. Find ways through activity to connect on the processing of feelings, but leaving them with positive skills for coping. Hopefully they feel more relaxed and will get in the habit of using those skills when they start having big feelings, whatever they may be.

I Love You More,
Robika, Rachael, and Anna

We would love to hear from you: how you use the book, questions, thoughts, etc. You can
email us at loveyoumorebooksllc@gmail.com

**Write and/or draw your thoughts and feelings
like Lala did when she was feeling different emotions.**

Write and/or draw your thoughts and feelings
like Lala did when she was feeling different emotions.

Write and/or draw your thoughts and feelings
like Lala did when she was feeling different emotions.

Write and/or draw your thoughts and feelings
like Lala did when she was feeling different emotions.